SELECTIVE MUSIC LISTS—1978

Full Orchestra

String Orchestra

Compiled by

Music Educators National Conference

and the

National School Orchestra Association

Music Educators National Conference
1902 Association Drive
Reston, Virginia 22091

Contents

iii

Foreword

In 1971 Music Educators National Conference published *Selective Music Lists: Band, Orchestra, and String Orchestra.* The listings for full orchestra and string orchestra were prepared by committees of the National School Orchestra Association (NSOA). The current publication is an update to the 1971 lists for orchestras. MENC is again grateful to the NSOA for reviewing the material.

The following NSOA members were on the Association's Continual Evaluation Committee during the period from 1971 to 1977 and consequently involved in this update: James H. Godfrey (committee chairman), Bowling Green, Kentucky; Laurens Blankers, Nashville; Ann-Lee Knobloch, Arlington, Virginia; Joe Klan, Louisville; Frederick Rosenzweig, Royal Oak, Michigan; and Clarence Blake, Falls Church, Virginia. MENC is also grateful to NSOA President John R. Bright for his assistance.

The committee and the MENC publications department staff have made every effort to ensure accuracy of titles and the names of composers and publishers. Special thanks is due to James Kellock, Dale Music Company, Silver Spring, Maryland, for his help in verifying this information. The committee also gave serious thought to the grading indicated. These gradings, however, should be regarded as no more than guides. Since it is not possible to include in a listing such as this all worthwhile materials, the reader is encouraged to study the catalogs of all publishers for further selections.

John Aquino
Director of Publications,
Editor, *MEJ*

Full Orchestra

Grade 1

Applebaum & Ployhar, arr.	Happy Sounds for Orchestra (Album)	Belwin-Mills
Bauernschmidt	Bear Mountain Polka	Lydian
Bruce	Tick-Tock Clock	Shawnee
Cruger/Spire, arr.	Now Thank We All Our God	Pro-Art
Frackenpohl	Air & Pizzicato-Staccato	Kendor
Frackenpohl	Intrada and Elegy	Kendor
Kabalevsky/Rowe, arr.	Five Happy Variations on a Russian Folksong	Pro-Art
Klauss	Choo Choo Caboo	Kendor
Langlitz	Pixie Dance	Kendor
Langlitz	Processional March	Etling
McBeth, arr.	Christmas in Concert	Alfred
Sanfilippo/Niehaus, arr.	Moreland Overture	Highland
Spire, arr.	Gypsy Dance	Pro-Art
Stephan & Ward	Project One for Young Orchestras of Today	Kendor
Stephan & Ward	Project Two for Young Orchestras of Today	Kendor

Grade 2

Alfven-Isaac	Swedish Rhapsody	Wynn
Bach/Bauernschmidt, arr.	Minuet (Concerto Grosso, Op. 6, No. 5)	Lydian
Bach/Eller, arr.	Two Bach Chorales	Shapiro-Bernstein
Bach/Gardner, arr.	Chorale: King of Glory	Staff
Bach/Gordon, arr.	Menuet, Aria, & Musette (Anna Magdalene's Notebook)	Shapiro-Bernstein
Bach/Gordon, arr.	Menuetto (Brandenburg Concerto No. 1)	Warner
Bach/Siennicki, arr.	Prelude	Etling
Bach/Stone, arr.	Menuet, Trios, and Polonaise (Brandenburg Concerto No. 1)	Oxford
Bach/Walter, arr.	Bach Triptych	Lydian
Bates/Muller, arr.	America the Beautiful Fantasy	Ludwig
Bauernschmidt, arr.	Arirang	Lydian
Bauernschmidt, arr.	A French Dance Suite	Lydian
Beethoven/Muller, arr.	Beethoven Selections	Kjos
Benoy, arr.	Prelude for Christmas	Oxford
Benoy, arr.	Scherzo for Christmas	Oxford
Christensen	Snow Chase	Leonard
Christensen	Variations on an Original Theme	Kendor
Cohan/Gordon, arr.	Star Spangled Spectacular	Marks
Corelli/Bauernschmidt, arr.	Largo from Concerto Grosse No. 1	Tempo
Corelli/Bauernschmidt, arr.	Suite from Sonata da Camera	Tempo
Couperin/Gordon, arr.	Baroque Dance Suite	Alfred

Cruger/Spire, arr.	Now Thank We All Our God	Pro-Art
Delibes/Brown, arr.	Pizzicati from the Ballet "Sylvia"	Pro-Art
Diamond-Cacavas, arr.	Holly Holy	Alfred
Eccles/Gordon, arr.	Queen Anne Suite	Alfred
Elgar/Gardner, arr.	Pomp and Circumstance March	Staff
Fahrer & Harry, arr.	Juilliard Repertory Library (Instrumental Vol. 4)	Canyon
Fink, arr.	Ben	Columbia
Fink, arr.	Bless the Beasts and the Children	Columbia
Forsblad & Livingston	Junior Philharmonic (Album)	Shawnee
Fote, arr.	British Grenadiers	Kendor
Fote, arr.	Holly Wreath Medley	Kendor
Frackenpohl	Air and Pizzicato-Staccato	Kendor
Frackenpohl	Intrada and Elegy	Kendor
Gluck/Bauernschmidt, arr.	Two Ballet Interludes	Tempo
Gordon, arr.	Haydn's Toy Symphony	Fischer
Gordon, arr.	Three Baroque Chorales	Kendor
Gordon, arr.	A Yuletide Festival	Warner
Gounod/Walter, arr.	Concert Waltz from Faust	Lydian
Guthrie/Ployhar, arr.	This Land Is Your Land	Leonard
Hajdu/Sandor-Till, arr.	Orchestral Etude No. 3	Boosey and Hawkes
Handel/Bauernschmidt, arr.	Minuet (Concerto Grosse Op. 6, No. 5)	Lydian
Handel/Christensen, arr.	Minuet and Trio in C Major	Pro-Art
Handel/Gordon, arr.	Firework Music	Shapiro-Bernstein
Handel/Rizzo, arr.	He Shall Feed His Flock	Kendor
Haydn/Bauernschmidt, arr.	Sinfonietta in G	Lydian
Haydn/Walter, arr.	Divertimento in G Major	Lydian
Herder	Spanish Montunos	A. Broude
Herfurth	Christmas March	Hansen
Herfurth & Stuart	Youth Symphony for Young Orchestras	Shawnee
Hirsch	Battle Ground	Tempo
Kabalevsky/Rowe, arr.	Five Happy Variations on a Russian Folksong	Pro-Art
Keller-Bruce	The American Hymn	Etling
Klauss, arr.	Two Pieces for Young Orchestras	Kendor
LeJeune/Gardner, arr.	Three 16th Century Chorales	Staff
Liadov/Stone, arr.	Russian Folksongs, Set II	Boosey and Hawkes
Magnusson, arr.	From the Land of Fire and Ice	Wynn
Marcello/Ployhar, arr.	Psalm and Air	Wynn
Martin-Pizzuto	Western Strings	Kendor
Matesky	Concertino for Violin	Alfred
Mozart/Gordon, arr.	The Sleigh Ride	Presser
Mussorgsky/Kohut, arr.	Coronation Chorus	Etling
Mussorgsky/Stone, arr.	The Great Gate of Kiev	Oxford
Obadia, arr.	Middle East Mood	Pro-Art
Osterling-Isaac	We Know Cha-Cha	Belwin-Mills
Palestrina/Gardner, arr.	Three Palestrina Chorales	Staff
Ployhar, arr.	Matilda (Calypso)	Wynn
Ployhar, arr.	Nobody Knows the Trouble I've Seen	Wynn

Ployhar, arr.	The Water Is Wide	Wynn
Purcell/Gardner, arr.	Trumpet Tune and Air	Staff
Rameau/Bauernschmidt, arr.	Le Tambourine Swings	Lydian
Rameau/Gordon, arr.	Village Dance	Kendor
Ravel/Ployhar, arr.	Pavane	Wynn
Reineke-Rhoads	Sonatina	Wynn
Rhoads, arr.	Circle of Stars	Wynn
Rhoads, arr.	Crinoline Ladies and Powdered Wigs	Wynn
Rhoads, arr.	European Christmas Festival	Wynn
Rhoads, arr.	Two Old Italian Vignettes	Wynn
Rodgers-O'Reilly	You'll Never Walk Alone	Alfred
Romeo	French Carousel	Pro-Art
Romeo	Surfside	Pro-Art
Romeo, arr.	God Rest You Merry Gentlemen	Pro-Art
Rusch	Folk Song Fantasy	Etling
Rusch, arr.	Chilean Folk Song	Tempo
Sanfilippo	El Burrito "Carlo"	Pro-Art
Scarmolin	Move Along	Ludwig
Sherman-Chase	It's a Small World	Hansen
Siennicki	Capriccio	Etling
Smetana/Brown, arr.	The Moldau	Pro-Art
Tchaikovsky/Gordon, arr.	Two Selections from "Album for the Young"	Kendor
Telemann/Bauernschmidt, arr.	Chaconne	Lydian
Telemann/Whitney, arr.	Air and Courante for Orchestra	Warner
Waldteufel/Benoy, arr.	Two Waltzes	Oxford
Walter, arr.	Cancion Mexicano	Lydian
Wilson, arr.	Kalocsai Csardas	Kendor
Wilson, arr.	Lakodalmi Tanc (Wedding Dance)	Kendor

Grade 3

Abel-Beechey	Symphony in E Flat	Oxford
Ades, arr.	Twentiana	Shawnee
Albert-Stephan	Feelings	Columbia
Bach/Errante, arr.	Fugue No. IV	Pro-Art
Bach/Frost, arr.	Little Suite from Anna Magdalena Notebook	A. Broude
Bach/Gearhart, arr.	Praeludium	Shawnee
Bach/Stone, arr.	Jesu, Joy of Man's Desiring	Oxford
Bauernschmidt	Perpetual Emotion	Tempo
Bauernschmidt, arr.	Folk Songs for Christmas	Lydian
Bauernschmidt, arr.	Three Spanish Carols	Lydian
Beethoven/Denny & Kerman, arr.	Two Orchestral Minuets	Oxford
Beethoven/Leidig, arr.	Finale (Beethoven's Ninth Symphony)	Wynn
Berlin/Ades, arr.	Irving Berlin—A Symphonic Portrait	Shawnee
Bizet/Stone, arr.	Carillon (L'Arlesienne Suite No. 1)	Boosey and Hawkes

Brahms/Isaac, arr.	Hungarian Dance No. 6	Etling
Brown	Hebraic Dance and Lament	Pro-Art
Brown	Russian Fantasy	Pro-Art
Burt/Ades, arr.	A Festival of Alfred Burt Carols	Shawnee
Cacavas	A Time for Kings	Belwin-Mills
Caldwell-Muller	Cycles	Leonard
Carey-Jurey & Graham, arr.	Land of Liberty (America)	Highland
Carmichael/Ployhar, arr.	Stardust	Belwin-Mills
Cassler, arr.	Wondrous Love	Schmitt
Chechvala	Slovakian Folk Song	Leonard
Clark	Overture, Prayer, and Dance	Etling
Clementi/Christensen, arr.	Allegro from Sonatina in C	Pro-Art
Clementi/Christensen, arr.	Rondo from Sonatina No. 5	Pro-Art
Corelli/Gordon, arr.	Little Suite for Orchestra	Fischer
Corelli/Lehmeier, arr.	Adagio and Allegro	Etling
Corelli/Livingston, arr.	Preludio e Danzetta	Lydian
Dalley	American Folk Scene	Hansen
Daniels	Cassation	Etling
Daniels	Sunfest	Ludwig
Dello Joio	The Dancing Sergeant	Belwin-Mills
Dvorak/Gardner, arr.	Psalm of Praise (from Symphony No. 4)	Staff
Dvorak/Isaac, arr.	Slavonic Dance No. 3	Etling
Dvorak/Isaac, arr.	Slavonic Dance No. 8	Etling
Eley	Prelude and Dance	Etling
Elliott & Stephens, arr.	Black Is the Color of My True Love's Hair	Wynn
Errante	Destino	Etling
Errante, arr.	Suite Chinois	Belwin-Mills
Fauré/Stone, arr.	Sicilienne (Pelléas et Mélisande)	Boosey and Hawkes
Fink, arr.	Nadia's Theme	Columbia
Forssmark	Larghetto	Shawnee
Gearhart, arr.	Overture on Jewish Themes	Shawnee
Gerard/Maltby, arr.	Butterfly	Leonard
Gordon	Aubade	Kendor
Grieg/Benoy, arr.	Symphonic Dance	Oxford
Grieg/Forsblad & Livingston, arr.	The Sounds of Norway	Leonard
Halvorsen/Isaac, arr.	March of the Boyars	Etling
Handel/Isaac, arr.	Judas Maccabaeus Suite	Etling
Hartley	Elizabethan Dances	Fema
Hastings, arr.	Folk Baroque Suite	Alfred
Haydn/Gordon, arr.	Haydn's Toy Symphony	Fischer
Haydn/Gordon, arr.	Symphony No. 20 in C (1st Mvt.)	Presser
Haydn/Isaac, arr.	Symphony No. 3 (1st Mvt.)	Etling
Haydn/Rizzo, arr.	Three German Dances	Kendor
Heinlen, arr.	The Trees of Christmas	Kendor
Herold/Lanchbury, arr.	Clog Dance	Oxford
Herold/Lanchbury, arr.	Flute Dance	Oxford
Holcombe	A Love for All Seasons	Musician's Publications

Hull	Contrasts for Orchestra	Wynn
Hull, arr.	Hispania	Wynn
Hummel/Brown, arr.	Hummel Concertante	Fischer
Isaac	Overture Russe	Fischer
Isaac, arr.	Espana Cani	Etling
Jager	Two Cherokee Impressions	Kendor
Jenkinson-Isaac	Moto Perpetuo	Etling
Johnson	Cortege	Kjos
Jost	Erzulie y Malade (Haitian Lament)	Lydian
Jurey	Bell Rondo	Highland
Kabalevsky/Brown, arr.	Kabalevsky Polka for Young Orchestra	MCA
Kabalevsky-Hastings	Kabalevskiana	Alfred
Kerman, Wm. & Joseph	Two Orchestra Minuets	Oxford
Knipper-Isaac	Meadowlands	Etling
Lai-Gordon	Theme from "Love Story"	Hansen
LeGrand/Fink, arr.	Brian's Song	Columbia
MacColl/Ployhar, arr.	The First Time Ever I Saw Your Face	Leonard
McLeod	Fiddlin' Fancy	Belwin-Mills
Matthews	Stonehenge	Etling
Mozart/Benoy, arr.	Andante and Presto (Divertimento K. 136)	Oxford
Mozart/Gordon, arr.	Ceremonial March	Elkan-Vogel
Mozart/Gordon, arr.	Menuetto from Symphony 25 in G Minor	Presser
Mozart/Isaac, arr.	Alleluia	Etling
Mozart/Isaac, arr.	Intrada	Highland
Mussorgsky/Bloodworth, arr.	Bydlo and Promenades Two and Three	Oxford
Nelhybel	Aegean Modes	Kerby
Nelhybel	Slavonic Triptych	Kerby
Ortolani-Oliviero/Gordon, arr.	Great Themes from Great Italian Movies	Marks
Popp-Arnold	Love Is Blue	Hansen
Prokofieff/Isaac, arr.	Troika (from Lt. Kijé Suite)	Fischer
Purcell/Gardner, arr.	Antiphonal Voluntary	Staff
Purcell/Gardner, arr.	Fanfare and Rondo	Staff
Rameau/Bauernschmidt, arr.	Le Tambourine Swings	Lydian
Raposa-Cleveland	Sing	Warner
Rieti	Old Time Polka from Recital for Young Chamber Players	General
Rieti	Tarantella from Recital for Young Chamber Players	General
Rimer	High Strung	Ludwig
Rizzo	Beguine for Barbara	Kendor
Rizzo, arr.	Breaking Up Is Hard to Do	Columbia
Rossini/Isaac, arr.	Petite Caprice	Etling
Rota-Gordon	Love Theme from "The Godfather"	Hansen
Sanfilippo	The Children's March	Pro-Art
Schillio, arr.	Festival of Lights	Pro-Art
Schmitt-Christensen	Rondo from Sonatina in C	Pro-Art
Schubert/Lehmeier, arr.	Unfinished Symphony, 1st Mvt. (abridged)	Etling

Seitz-Isaac	Concerto No. 2 (3rd Mvt.)	Etling
Siennicki	Strawberry Fluff	Etling
Stamitz/Siennicki, arr.	Allegro	Etling
Stokowski, arr.	Traditional Slavic Christmas Music	A. Broude
Strouse/Lang, arr.	Musical Highlights from "Annie"	Big Three
Swack	Brief Journey	Presser
Tartini/Bauernschmidt, arr.	Fantasia for Orchestra	Lydian
Telemann/Bauernschmidt, arr.	Overture in G Dur	Lydian
Telemann/Errante, arr.	Concerto in A Minor	Etling
Telemann/Livingston, arr.	Cappricietto	Lydian
Telemann/Walter, arr.	Zwei Stücke	Lydian
Tschaikowsky/Isaac, arr.	Capriccio Italien	Etling
Tschaikowsky/Lehmeier, arr.	Overture 1812	Etling
Wagner/Siennicki, arr.	Die Meistersinger	Ludwig
Washburn	Ode to Freedom	Oxford
Webb/Muller, arr.	MacArthur Park	Warner
Webber/Muller, arr.	I Didn't Know How to Love Him	Leeds
von Weber/Gordon, arr.	Three Rustic Dances	Kendor
Weeks	Shades of Agora	Shawnee
Williams-Cacavas	Suite from "Jaws"	MCA
Winkler-Reed	Testament of an American	Belwin-Mills
Yon/Ployhar, arr.	Gesu Bambino	Belwin-Mills

Grade 4

Bach/Brown, arr.	Sleepers Awake	Pro-Art
Bach/Hanspeter, arr.	Sinfonia, Op. 6, No. 1 in G Major	Edition Peters
Bartow	Summershadow	Shawnee
Beck-Tatgenhorst	Variants on an Irish Hymn	Presser
Berger	Creole Overture for Orchestra	Schirmer
Berlioz/Carter, arr.	March to the Scaffold	Oxford
Bilik	American Civil War Fantasy	Southern-NY
Bissell	Andante e Scherzo	Kerby
Bizet/Stone, arr.	Overture to "Dr. Miracle"	Oxford
Borodin/Isaac, arr.	Symphony No. 2 (1st Mvt.)	Etling
Brahms/Gearhart, arr.	Adagio Op. 111	Shawnee
Buxtehude/Fink, arr.	Chaconne in E Minor	Columbia
Caruso	A Child Remembering	Elkan-Vogel
Cassler, arr.	The Turtle Dove	Schmitt
Coker	Declarative Essay	Presser
Dankworth	Tom Sawyer's Saturday	Oxford
Danzi/Forster, arr.	Konzert No. 4	Edition Peters
Dimler/Balassa & Fodor, arr.	Konzert in B♭	Edition Peters
Dittersdorf/Jerger, arr.	Esther	Doblinger Associated
Faith	Elegy	Schirmer

Faith	Quia Quia	Leonard
Fauré/Gearhart, arr.	Pavane	Shawnee
Fote	The Blues	Kendor
Friedman/Lehmeier, arr.	Windy	Leonard
Fry	Triptych	Fischer
Gordon	Little Suite for Orchestra	Fischer
Handel/Pinkham, arr.	Forest Music	Schirmer
Harris, arr.	Americana	A. Broude
Haydn, J./Landon, arr.	Acide e Galatea	Doblinger Associated
Haydn, J./Landon, arr.	Lo Speziale	Doblinger Associated
Haydn, J./Landon, arr.	Menuetti Ballabili	Doblinger Associated
Haydn, J./Landon, arr.	Ouverture in D-Dur	Doblinger Associated
Haydn, J./Landon, arr.	Sinfonia in D-Dur	Doblinger Associated
Haydn, J./Landon, arr.	Te Deum	Doblinger Associated
Haydn, M.	Sinfonia in E Flat	Doblinger Associated
Haydn, M.	Sinfonia in G	Doblinger Associated
Haydn, M.	Sinfonia in D	Doblinger Associated
Hayes/Lowden, arr.	Selections from "Shaft"	Big Bells
Hoag	An After-Intermission Overture	Schirmer
Holcombe	American Celebration	Musician's Publications
Ives/Kirkpatrick, arr.	Fugue in Four Keys on "The Shining Shore"	Presser
Jacob	A Noyse of Minstrells	Oxford
Klauss	Elegy for Chamber Orchestra	Tempo
Klauss	Two Moods	Kendor
LeGrand/Muller, arr.	Theme from "Summer of '42"	Warner
Liszt/Gordon, arr.	Consolation No. 3	Fischer
Lowden, arr.	Musical Highlights from "Rocky"	Big Three
Lowden, arr.	Sounds of The Carpenters	Big Bells
Luening	Kentucky Rondo	Galaxy
MacLellan-Schaefer	Snowbird	Leonard
Mancini, arr.	Medley from "Jesus Christ Superstar"	MCA
Matesky	Choreo Primo	Kjos
Mauret & Parnes/Lowden, arr.	The Masterpiece	Big Bells
McGlohon-Fote	Waltz for a Ballerina Doll	Kendor
McKay, arr.	Fantasy on a Quiet Theme	Shawnee
Miller-Murden	For Once in My Life	Belwin-Mills
Mitchell	Sing America	Marks
Mozart/Isaac, arr.	A Musical Sleigh Ride	Highland

Mozart/Riessberger, arr.	Jagd-Sinfonie	Doblinger Associated
Muller, arr.	Scarborough Fair	Leonard
Nelhybel	A Mighty Fortress	Kerby
Pankow-Schaefer	Colour My World	Leonard
Petersen, arr.	I'd Like to Teach the World to Sing	Kendor
Polster, arr.	That's Entertainment	Big Three
Prokofieff/Isaac, arr.	Romeo and Juliet Suite	Fischer
Prokofieff/Isaac, arr.	The Wedding of Lt. Kijé	Fischer
Putman-Schaefer	Green Grass of Home	Leonard
Rimsky-Korsakov/Isaac, arr.	Procession of the Nobles	Etling
Rusch, arr.	Struttin' Strings	Highland
Rutter	Shepherd's Pipe Carol	Oxford
Schaefer	Shadings	Columbia
Schaefer, arr.	I'd Like to Teach the World to Sing	Leonard
Schaefer, arr.	Rainy Days and Mondays	Leonard
Schickele	Celebration with Bells	Elkan-Vogel

Schubert/Niehaus & Leidig,
  arr.
	Schubert's C Major Symphony
	  (1st Mvt.)
		Highland

Shostakovich/Isaac, arr.	Prelude	Etling
Sibelius/Leidig, arr.	Sibelius Second Symphony (4th Mvt.)	Highland
Siennicki	Orchestral Variations	Concert Music
Smith	Fanfare and Celebration	Wingert-Jones
Sousa/Stokowski, arr.	The Stars and Stripes Forever	A. Broude
Stevens-Lehmeier	Everything Is Beautiful	Leonard
Stravinsky/Isaac, arr.	Danse Infernale	Belwin-Mills
Takacs	Serenade	Associated
Thomson	Boy Fights Alligator	Schirmer

Ulrich	High School Symphony for Winds,
	  Strings, Percussion and Piano
	  (or Harpsichord)
		Schirmer

Vaughan Williams/Foster, arr.	Rhosymedre	Galaxy
Vivaldi/Isaac, arr.	Concerto Grosso in D Minor	Etling
Wagner-Mayer	Tannhauser (Extended Finale)	Southern-Texas
Washburn	Excursion for Orchestra	Oxford
Webb-Lehmeier	By the Time I Get to Phoenix	Leonard
Whear	White River Legend	Ludwig

Grade 5

Adler	City by the Lake	Schirmer
Bach, J. C./Hanspeter, arr.	Sinfonia (Overture) Op. 3, No. 1 in D Major	Edition Peters
Bales	American Design	A. Broude
Beethoven	Zwolf Menuette	Edition Eulenburg
Berger	Short Symphony	Boonin
Binkerd, arr.	Four Choral Preludes	Boosey and Hawkes
Bruckner/Schonzeler, arr.	Four Kleine Orchesterstücke	Edition Peters

Copland	Prairie Journal	Boosey and Hawkes
Cowell	Carol for Orchestra	Associated
Harris, arr.	Christmas, A Medley of Well-Known Carols	A. Broude
Hartley	Variations for Orchestra	Fema
Hovhaness	Symphony No. 22 "City of Light"	Edition Peters
Ives	Fugue (from Symphony No. 4)	Associated
Ives/Singleton, arr.	March III	Presser
Leigh-Lang	Man of La Mancha Selections	Fox
Muczynski	Charade for Orchestra, Op. 28	Schirmer
Shaefer	The Sound of America	Leonard
Smith/Stokowski, arr.	The Star Spangled Banner	A. Broude
Szervánszky	Serenade	Boosey and Hawkes
Vaughan Williams	The Wasps	Schirmer
Villa-Lobos/Krance, arr.	Aria (Cantilena) from Bachianas Brasileiras No. 5	Associated
Washburn	Festive Overture	Oxford
Washburn	Prologue and Dance	Oxford
Williams/Burden, arr.	Star Wars Medley	Columbia

Grade 6

Becker	Symphonia Brevis (Symphony No. 3)	Peters
Biscogli	Concerto	Peters
Chou-Wen-chung	Pien	Peters
Finney	Three Pieces	Peters
Freedman	Tangents for Orchestra	Leeds
Ives	The Fourth of July	Associated (rental)
Ives/Sinclair, arr.	County Band March	Presser
Kay	Theater Set for Orchestra	MCA
Kraft	Contextures: Riots-Decade '60	Leeds
LaMontaine	Jubilant Overture, Op. 20	Fischer (rental)
Lutoslawski	Livre Pour Orchestre	Chester
Martinon	Symphony No. 4 (Altitudes)	Presser
Meiner	Symphony No. 1, Op. 18	MCA
Nelson	Rocky Point Holiday	Boosey and Hawkes
Ortolani-Oliviero/Hayman, arr.	"More" Theme from "Mondo Cane"	Marks
Sapieyevski	Summer Overture	Mercury (rental)
Siegmeister	Five Fantasies of the Theater	MCA
Siegmeister	Western Suite in Five Movements	MCA
Stephens	Danse de España	Highland
Strauss, J./Schweiger, arr.	The Gypsy Baron Suite	Boosey and Hawkes
Walker	Address for Orchestra	MCA (rental)
Ward	Invocation and Toccata	Highgate
Wiener	Fantasie Concertante for Double Bass and Orchestra	Broude (rental)
Zador	Studies for Orchestra	Chester

String Orchestra

Grade 1

Albert/Forsblad, arr.	Feelings	Leonard
Caponegro	Canyon Sunset	Kendor
Caponegro	Fumble Fingers	Kendor
Errante, arr.	Ten Pieces for String Orchestra	Shawnee
Ewing, arr.	A Suite Christmas	Kendor
Gordon	Sunshine and Shadow	Fox
Hamlisch/Fink, arr.	The Way We Were	Columbia
Hanby-Wieloszynski	Up on the House-Top	Kendor
Hodkinson	Drawings Set No. 7	Presser
Hubbell	Two by Two	Etling
Klauss	The Cat and the Fiddle	Kendor
Klauss	Loch Lomond	Kendor
Klein-Fote	The Children's Waltz	Kendor
Klotman & Burkhalter	String Literature for Expanding Technique	Fema
Martin-Pizzuto	Western Strings	Kendor
Mozart/Phillips, arr.	Minuet in D Minor	Kendor
Peck	Winter Music	Belwin-Mills
Stoutamire-Henderson, arr.	Stringing Along (Album)	Pro-Art
Sutherland & Rofe	Simple String Pieces	Marks
Wieloszynski, arr.	Jolly Old St. Nicholas	Kendor
Williams	Southwestern Suite	Southern-Texas

Grade 2

Applebaum & Gordon	Tribute to John Philip Sousa	Belwin-Mills
Avison/Isaac, arr.	Concerto in E Minor	Etling
Bach/Siekmann, arr.	Menuet	Kendor
Bach/Siennicki, arr.	Chorale and March	Etling
Barclay	The Mission at Santa Fe	Barger-Barclay
Bartók/Gordon, arr.	A Little Bartók Suite	Fischer
Beckwith	Fall Scene and Fair Dance	BMI Canada
Benoy, arr.	A Second Book for the Young Orchestra	Oxford
Benson	Theme and Excursions	Fema
Binge	Simple Serenade	Belwin-Mills
Bolzoni/Isaac, arr.	Minuetto	Etling
Brahms/Appleby & Fowler, arr.	Seven Pieces by Brahms	Oxford
Caponegro	Fiddling A-Round	Kendor
Caponegro	Rhumbolero	Kendor
Casals	Song of the Birds	A. Broude
Chase/Applebaum, arr.	An American Suite	Belwin-Mills
Chase, arr.	Eleanor Rigby	Chappell
Chase, arr.	Let It Be	Chappell
Chase, arr.	Norwegian Wood	Chappell
Chase, arr.	The Long and Winding Road	Chappell
Chase, arr.	Jingle, Jangle, Jingle	Hansen

D'Hervelois-Abbott	Musette	Kendor
DiLasso/Klotman, arr.	Echo Fantasy for Double String Orchestra	Fema
Dodd/Higgins, arr.	Mickey Mouse March	Leonard
Ellmenreich-Siennicki	Spinning Song	Etling
Fink, arr.	Black and White	Columbia
Fink, arr.	Bless the Beasts and the Children	Columbia
Fink, arr.	Nadia's Theme	Columbia
Forsblad	Axiom	Leonard
Forsblad, arr.	Never Smile at a Crocodile	Leonard
Frackenpohl	Air and Pizzicato-Staccato	Kendor
Frost	Caprice	Southern-Texas
Frost	Chimes	Kendor
Frost	Dance Conversations	Southern-Texas
Frost	Dreams	Kendor
Frost	Driftwood	Kendor
Frost	Hornpipe for String Orchestra	Southern-Texas
Frost	Joy	Kendor
Gearhart	String Mix No. I (Album)	Shawnee
Giammario	Five Carols for Christmas	Musician's Publications
Godla	Chamber Music for Guitar & Strings	Kjos
Gordon	Sunshine and Shadow	Fox
Gordon, arr.	Three Baroque Chorales	Kendor
Grant	The Scarlet Sarafan	Ludwig
Handel/Applebaum, arr.	Chamber Suite in D	Belwin-Mills
Handel/Isaac, arr.	Harmonious Blacksmith Suite	Etling
Handel/Siennicki, arr.	Little Fugue	Etling
Handel/Sontag, arr.	Menuet and Trio—Bourree	Sheffield
Hayman/Young-Muller, arr.	When I Fall in Love	MCA
Higgins, arr.	The Candy Man	Leonard
Hodkinson	Drawings Set No. 8	Presser
Isaac	Walking Basses	Etling
Isaac	Rhythm and Styles (Folio)	Etling
Isaac	Quinto-Quarto Suite	Etling
Isaac	The Apollo Suite	Etling
Isaac, arr.	Down by the Riverside	Etling
Jaffe	Short Suite for String Orchestra	Southern-Texas
Jones/Applebaum, arr.	English Folk Song Suite	Belwin-Mills
Keller	Serenade for Clarinet & Strings	Fischer
Klauss	String Jamboree	Kendor
Klauss	Loch Lomond	Kendor
von Kreisler	Divertimento for Strings	Southern-Texas
Kriechbaum	Petite Tango	Etling
Leyden	Serenade for String Orchestra	Plymouth
Lichner-Siennicki	Sonatina	Etling
Martin-Pizzuto	Gypsy Strings	Kendor
Martin-Pizzuto	Western Strings	Kendor
McLeod	Golden Melodies for Strings I & II	Schmitt
Mlynarski-Applebaum	Mazurka	Belwin-Mills

Mozart/Isaac, arr.	Andante and Allegro	Etling
Mozart/Phillips, arr.	Minuet in D Minor	Kendor
Muller	Dawn of Peace	Kjos
Muller/Fink, arr.	Valse Moderne	Shawnee
Muller, arr.	Caravan	Belwin-Mills
Muller, arr.	Hey Mr. Banjo	Belwin-Mills
Muller, arr.	Red Roses for a Blue Lady	Belwin-Mills
Muller, arr.	Rock A Bye Your Baby with a Dixie Melody	Belwin-Mills
Rameau/Gordon, arr.	Village Dance	Kendor
Ravel/Isaac, arr.	Pavane	Fischer
Rezso-Sandor-Till	Orchestral Etudes No. 2	Boosey and Hawkes
Rhoads, arr.	Antique Dance Suite	Wynn
Rodgers/Forsblad, arr.	Do-Re-Mi	Leonard
Rouse-Muller	Orange Blossom Special	MCA
Schmidt/Forsblad, arr.	Try to Remember	Leonard
Schramm	Mogul Set	Boosey and Hawkes
Siennicki	Camels and Kings	Kjos
Siennicki, arr.	In Praise of Christmas	Etling
Somers	Little Suite for String Orchestra	Berandol
Tchaikovsky/Gordon, arr.	Two Selections from "Album for the Young"	Kendor
Vincent, arr.	Baroque Album	Highland
von Weber/Gordon, arr.	Three Rustic Dances	Kendor
von Weber/Isaac, arr.	The Weber Suite	Etling
Williamson	The Bridge that Van Gogh Painted	Marks
Williamson	Two Pieces for String Orchestra	Belwin-Mills

Grade 3

Albert-Stephan	Feelings	Columbia
Alshin	Macumba	Belwin-Mills
Applebaum, arr.	The Little Drummer Boy	Belwin-Mills
Bach/Herfurth, arr.	Arioso (Kantate No. 156)	Fischer
Bach/Isaac, arr.	Brandenburg Concerto No. 3	Etling
Bales	Music of the American Revolution	Peer
Barclay & LeGrand/ Muller, arr.	Once Upon a Summertime	MCA
Becaud/Muller, arr.	Let It Be Me	MCA
Beethoven/Isaac, arr.	Minuetto and Country Dance	Etling
Betti-Muller	C'est Si Bon	MCA
Biber-Currier	Partita for Strings	Kendor
Binkerd, arr.	Five Transcriptions for String Orchestra	Boosey and Hawkes
Brahms/Isaac, arr.	Hungarian Dance No. 6	Etling
Coakley	Directions North	Kerby
Daniels	Pendleton Suite	Etling
Daninov-Phillips	Three Bagatelles	Kendor
Debussy/Isaac, arr.	Clair de Lune	Etling
Doyle-Coons	Scarlet Tree	Kendor
Eccles/Isaac, arr.	Prelude and Courante	Etling

Feese	Colorado Suite	Young World
Feese	Festival at Newport	Young World
Feese	Red Rocks Suite	Young World
Feese	Winter Soliloquy	Young World
Franck-Corina	Four Short Pieces	Southern-Texas
Frost	Festival for Fiddlers	Southern-Texas
Gordon	Aubade	Kendor
Gordon	Prelude and Fugue in E Minor	Belwin-Mills
Gordon	A Yuletide Festival	Warner
Grant	Woodside Suite	Ludwig
Hatch-Muller	Call Me	MCA
Hovhaness	Armenian Rhapsody No. 3	Peters
Isaac, arr.	Early American Suite	Etling
Járdányi	Sinfonietta	Boosey and Hawkes
Kaempfert/Muller, arr.	Strangers in the Night	MCA
Kenins	Nocturne and Dance	Boosey and Hawkes
King-Muller	The Hawaiian Wedding Song	Pickwick
Klauss	Lullaby	Kendor
Lai-Arnold	Theme from "Love Story"	Hansen
LeGrand/Fink, arr.	Brian's Song	Columbia
Marcello-Siennicki	Marcello Suite	Etling
Marchetti-Isaac	Fascination	Etling
Marquina-Knight	Espani Cani	Marks
Mazas/Rothrock, arr.	Mazas, Op. 38, No. 2	Musician's Publications
Morgan	Suite: Love and Honour	Oxford
Moussorgsky/Isaac, arr.	Hopak	Etling
Mozart/Landon, arr.	Sinfonia in B Dur	Doblinger Associated
Muller, arr.	I Wish You Love	MCA
Nestico	Ballerina	Kendor
Pachelbel/Ades, arr.	Canon for Strings	Shawnee
Purcell/Isaac, arr.	Rondeau and Chaconne	Etling
Rhoads, arr.	Les Folies D'Espagne	Wynn
Rizzo, arr.	Breaking Up Is Hard to Do	Columbia
Seitz-Isaac	Concerto No. 2 (3rd Mvt.)	Etling
Sumerlin	Three Pieces for String Orchestra	Southern-Texas
Telemann/Bauernschmidt, arr.	Overture in G Dur	Lydian

Grade 4

Anderson-Applebaum	Fiddle-Faddle	Belwin-Mills
Anderson-Applebaum	Sleigh Ride	Belwin-Mills
Anderson-Applebaum	The Syncopated Clock	Belwin-Mills
Beglarian	Sinfonia for Strings	Belwin-Mills
Berger	Divertissment	Schirmer
Bissell	Divertimento for String Orchestra	Boonin
Cacavas, arr.	Christmas Music	Bourne
Chescoe	Conversation Piece	Associated
Cordero	Adagio Tragico	Peer
Dietrich	Concertino Giocoso	Associated
Faith	Pizzicato Polka	Leonard
Feese	Bon Bons 'n Bossa	Young World
Gesben	Colloquy for Strings	Warner
Hayman, arr.	More	Marks
Holesovsky, arr.	The Shadow of Your Smile	Big Three
Joplin-Muller	Medley from "The Sting"	MCA
Kodály/Bloodworth & Fluck, arr.	Four Dances (from Gyermektancok)	Boosey and Hawkes
Mendelssohn	Sinfonia in F—No. XI	DVFM/A. Broude
Mendelssohn	Sinfonia in C—No. IX	DVFM/A. Broude
Mendelssohn/Henderson, arr.	Song of the Heather	Kendor
Merrill-Holesovsky	Selections from "Carnival"	Big Three
Muller, arr.	Lennon and McCartney for String Orchestra	Warner
Muller, arr.	Beatlemania for Strings	Warner
Newman/Muller, arr.	Airport Love Theme	Leeds
Rickey, arr.	If We Only Have Love	Big Three
Rubinstein, arr.	Seven Miniatures for String Orchestra	Shawnee
Rutter	Shepherd Pipe Carol	Oxford
Satie/Klotman, arr.	Gymnopedies	Marks
Stoker	Chorale for Strings	A. Broude
Symonds	Pastel Blue	Kerby
Thielemans/Muller, arr.	Bluesette	MCA
Velke	Adagietto for Strings	Things for Strings
Vitali-Bacon	Suite for String Orchestra	Fox
White	Divertisement No. 2	Ludwig

Grade 5

Bales	Stony Brook	Southern-NY
Bissell	Three Pieces	Kerby
Cohrssen-Applebaum	Essay for Strings	Belwin-Mills
Coulthard	A Prayer for Elizabeth	Berandol
Dahl	Variations on a Theme by C.P.E. Bach	A. Broude
Harris	Chorale for Strings	Shawnee
Lee	Earth Genesis	Hansen
Montsalvatge	Tres Danzas Concertantes	Southern-NY
Racek	Tema Con Variazioni	Associated
Reigger	Canon and Fugue for Strings	Shawnee
Serly	String Symphony in Four Cycles	Southern-NY
Shulman	Threnody for String Orchestra	Tetra
Szervánszky	Serenade for String Orchestra	Boosey and Hawkes
Warlock	Serenade for Strings	Oxford

Grade 6

Laderman	Celestial Bodies	Oxford
Prokofiev/Barschai, arr.	Visions Fugitives, Op. 22	A. Broude
Serebrier	Momento Psicologico	Peer
Serebrier	Variations on a Theme from Childhood	Peer
Steffan/Picton, arr.	Concerto in D Major	Oxford

Directory of Publishers

Alfred Music Company, Inc.—15335 Morrison Street, Sherman Oaks, California 91403

Associated Music Publishers, Inc.—866 Third Avenue, New York City 10022

Barger-Barclay—1325 Orange Isle, Fort Lauderdale, Florida 33315

Berandol Music, Ltd.—11 St. Joseph Street, Toronto, Ontario, Canada M4Y 1J8

Belwin-Mills Publishing Corporation—25 Deshon Drive, Melville, New York 11746

Big Bells, Inc.—33 Hovey Avenue, Trenton, New Jersey 08610

Big Three Music Corporation—729 Seventh Avenue, New York City 10019

BMI Canada—See Berandol Music, Ltd.

Boonin, Joseph, Inc.—European American Music, 195 Allwood Road, Clifton, New Jersey 07012

Boosey and Hawkes, Inc.—P.O. Box 130, Oceanside, New York 11572

Bourne Company—866 Third Avenue, New York City 10022

Broude, A., Inc.—225 West Fifty-seventh Street, New York City 10019

Broude Brothers, Ltd.—56 West Forty-fifth Street, New York City 10036

Canyon Press—P.O. Box 1235, Cincinnati 45201

Chappell and Company, Inc.—See Theodore Presser Company

Chester, J. and W., Ltd.—See G. Schirmer, Inc.

Columbia Pictures Publications—16333 N.W. Fifty-fourth Avenue, Hialeah, Florida 33014

Concert Music—See Studio P/R, Inc.

Doblinger Associated—See Associated Music Publishers, Inc.

DVFM/A. Broude—225 West Fifty-seventh Street, New York City 10019

Edition Eulenburg, Inc.—See C. F. Peters Corporation

Edition Peters—See C. F. Peters Corporation

Elkan-Vogel Publishing Company—Bryn Mawr, Pennsylvania 19010

Etling Publishing Company—1790 Joseph Court, Elgin, Illinois 60120

Fema Music Publications—P.O. Box 395, Naperville, Illinois 60540

Fischer, Carl, Inc.—56-62 Cooper Square, New York City 10003

Fox, Sam, Publishing Company, Inc.—P.O. Box 850, Valley Forge, Pennsylvania 19482

Galaxy Music Corporation—2121 Broadway, New York City 10023

General Music Publishing Company—See G. Schirmer, Inc.

Hansen Publications, Inc.—1860 Broadway, New York City 10023

Highgate Publishing Company—See Galaxy Music Corporation

Highland Music Company—1311 North Highland Avenue, Hollywood, California 90028

Kendor Music, Inc.—Delevan, New York 14042

Kerby, E. C., Ltd.—198 Davenport Road, Toronto, Ontario, Canada M5R 1J2

Kjos, Neil A., Music Company—4382 Jutland Drive, San Diego 92117

Leeds Music—See Belwin-Mills Publishing Corporation

Leonard, Hal, Publishing Corporation—960 East Mark Street, Winona, Minnesota 55987

Ludwig Music Publishing Company—557-567 East 140th Street, Cleveland, Ohio 44110

Lydian Orchestrations—31000 Ruth Hill Road, Orange Cove, California 93646

Marks, Edward B., Music Corporation—25 Deshon Drive, Melville, New York 11746

MCA Music Company—25 Deshon Drive, Melville, New York 11746

Mercury Music Corporation—See Theodore Presser Company

Musician's Publications—P.O. Drawer 7160, West Trenton, New Jersey 08628

Oxford University Press—200 Madison Avenue, New York City 10016

Peer International—1740 Broadway, New York City 10019

Peters, C. F., Corporation—373 Park Avenue South, New York City 10016

Pickwick Music Company—See MCA Music Company

Plymouth Music Company, Inc.—17 West Sixtieth Street, New York City 10023

Presser, Theodore, Company—Presser Place, Bryn Mawr, Pennsylvania 19010

Pro-Art Publishing Company—See Belwin-Mills Publishing Corporation

Schirmer, G., Inc.—866 Third Avenue, New York City 10022

Schmitt Music Publications—110 North Fifth Street, Minneapolis, Minnesota 55403

Shapiro-Bernstein & Company—See Plymouth Music Company, Inc.

Shawnee Press, Inc.—Delaware Water Gap, Pennsylvania 18327

Sheffield Music Corporation—See Plymouth Music Company, Inc.

Southern Music Company—P.O. Box 329, San Antonio, Texas 78292

Southern Music Publishing Company—1740 Broadway, New York City 10019

Staff Music Company—See Plymouth Music Company, Inc.

Studio P/R, Inc.—224 South Lebanon Street, Lebanon, Indiana 46052

Tempo Music Company—P.O. Box 392, Chicago, Illinois 60690

Tetra Music Corporation—See A. Broude, Inc.

Things for Strings Publishing Company—P.O. Box 9263, Alexandria, Virginia 22304

Warner Brothers Music Company—75 Rockefeller Plaza, Fourteenth Floor, New York City 10019

Wingert-Jones Music, Inc.—P.O. Box 1878, Kansas City, Missouri 64141

Wynn Music Publishing Company—P.O. Box 739, Orinda, California 94563

Young World Publications—10485 Glennon Drive, Lakewood, Colorado 80226